CGP is top of the charts for SATs prep!

This SAT Buster Book 2 is bursting with more practice for the KS2 Maths SATs Reasoning papers — it covers Geometry, Measures and Statistics.

It's bursting with questions covering all the skills pupils need, with friendly self-assessment boxes to record how confident they feel about each topic.

We've even included a handy scoresheet at the back, so it's easy to keep track of their marks for the whole book. Brilliant!

What CGP is all about

Our sole aim here at CGP is to produce the highest quality books
— carefully written, immaculately presented and
dangerously close to being funny.

Then we work our socks off to get them out to you
— at the cheapest possible prices.

Published by CGP

Editors: Samuel Mann and Caroline Purvis

ISBN: 978 1 78908 138 1

With thanks to Ruth Greenhalgh for the proofreading.
Also thanks to Laura Jakubowski for the copyright research.

Printed by Bell & Bain Ltd, Glasgow.
Clipart from Corel®

Based on the classic CGP style created by Richard Parsons.

Contents

Section 1 - Geometry

Section 2 - Measurement

Section 3 - Statistics

Here's what you have to do...

In Year 6 you have to take some tests called the SATs. This book will help you do well in the geometry, measures & statistics questions on the maths tests.

This is a Trimeasuretops — it can handle even the trickiest maths questions.

Your aim is to become a Trimeasuretops.

Work through the questions in the book. When you finish a topic, add up your marks and write them in the scoresheet at the end of the book.

Then, put a tick in the box at the end of the topic to show how you got on.

If you got a lot of questions wrong, put a tick in the circle on the left. Don't worry — every Trimeasuretops has to start somewhere. Make sure you know your geometry, measures and statistics rules inside out, then have another go.

If you're nearly there but your maths is still a bit wobbly, put a tick in the middle circle. Ask your teacher to help you work out the areas you need more practice on.

If you're really confident and got nearly all the questions right, tick the circle on the right.

Congratulations — you're a Trimeasuretops!

2D Shapes

Have a go at these questions to see how much you can remember about 2D shapes.

1) Which shape is being described below? Circle your answer.

   It has four sides.
   All sides are the same length.
   It has no right angles.

   Square   Equilateral Triangle   Rhombus   Regular Hexagon   _____

1 mark

2) Look at the shapes below. Circle the shape that has more than one right angle.
    Put a cross through the shape that has no pairs of parallel sides.

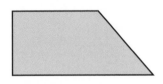 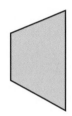 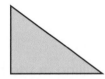 

   _____
   2 marks

3) Here is part of a shape.

   Draw more straight lines to
   make it into a **parallelogram**.

   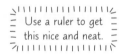
   Use a ruler to get
   this nice and neat.

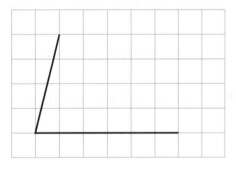

   _____
   1 mark

4) Are these statements true or false? Circle the answers.

   A pentagon can never have perpendicular sides.   **TRUE / FALSE**

   An isosceles triangle has no equal angles.   **TRUE / FALSE**

   A trapezium has one pair of parallel sides.   **TRUE / FALSE**   _____

2 marks

5) Look at the shape on the grid.

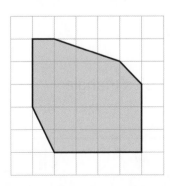

   How many sides does this shape have?   ☐

   How many pairs of parallel sides
   does this shape have?   ☐

   _____
   2 marks

2D Shapes

6) This is a sorting diagram. The shapes below need to be sorted. Complete the diagram by writing the letters in the right places.

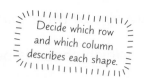

Decide which row and which column describes each shape.

	All angles equal	Not all angles equal
Has at least two sides of equal length	....	....
Has no sides of equal length	....	....

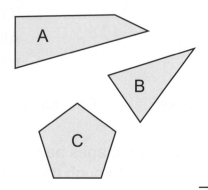

1 mark

7) Complete the sentences by filling in the blanks.

A .... triangle has no equal sides or angles.

A .... shape has sides of equal length and equal angles.

A kite has .... pair(s) of equal sides and .... line(s) of symmetry.

2 marks

8) Manon has drawn a picture using some 2D shapes.

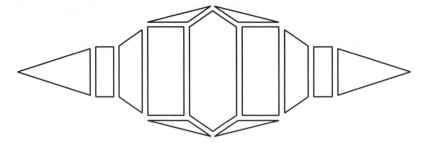

Which of the shapes below has Manon **not** used in her picture? Circle your answer.

Hexagon   Trapezium   Square   Isosceles triangle

1 mark

Circles

Now it's time to test your knowledge of circles. Give these questions a go.

1) Here is a circle with three parts labelled.
   Match each label to the correct word.

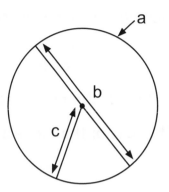

| a |

| radius |

| b |

| circumference |

| c |

| diameter |

_____
2 marks

2) Fill in the missing lengths on these circles.

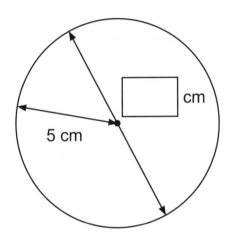

cm

5 cm

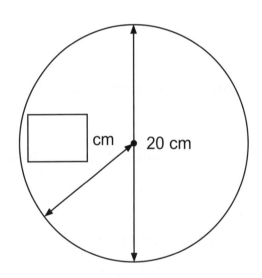

cm

20 cm

Not drawn
accurately

_____
2 marks

3) Sandy is building a model bike.
   The design of one of the wheels is shown in the diagram.

   The wheel is a circle with a diameter of **12 cm**.
   It also has **five** spokes, which go from
   the centre of the circle to the edge.

   What is the **sum** of the lengths of all five spokes?
   Show your working in the box.

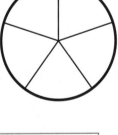

12 cm

Not drawn
accurately

.... cm

_____
2 marks

A Trimeasuretops doesn't go round in circles —
they get straight to the answer. How did you do?

Section 1 — Geometry

3D Shapes

Try these questions to see how much you know about 3D shapes.

1) Match each description to the shape it describes. One has been done for you.

It has ten faces. **Two of the faces are octagons.** **The rest of the faces are rectangles.**	**Cylinder**
It has four faces. **All the faces are identical triangles.**	*The faces at the two ends of a prism are exactly the same shape.* **Octagonal prism**
It has six faces. **All the faces are rectangles.**	**Triangular-based pyramid**
It has two identical circular faces.	**Cuboid**

2 marks

2) This shape is a pentagonal prism.

How many vertices does a pentagonal prism have?

.... *vertices*

1 mark

3) This is the net of a 3D shape.

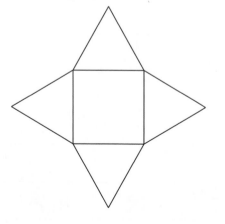

What kind of shape is this the net for?

....

How many edges will the 3D shape have?

.... *edges*

2 marks

3D Shapes

4) Part of the net of a cube has been drawn on the grid below.

    Shade one more square on the grid to show where the last face could be.

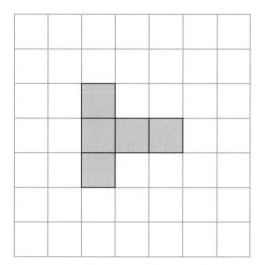

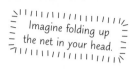

Imagine folding up the net in your head.

_____

1 mark

5) A model of a house is made by joining
    a **square-based pyramid** to the top of a **cuboid**.

    How many faces does this model house have?

.... *faces*

_____

1 mark

6) Complete the prisms on the grid below using a ruler.
    One has been done for you.

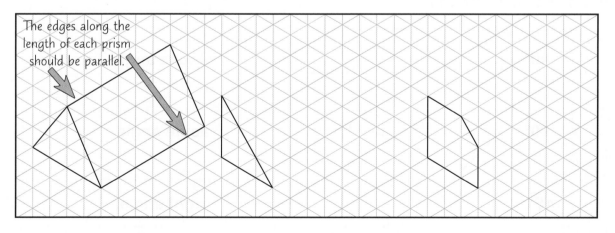

The edges along the length of each prism should be parallel.

_____

2 marks

Angles

Here are some questions on the different types of angles and how to measure them.

1) Look at the angles below.

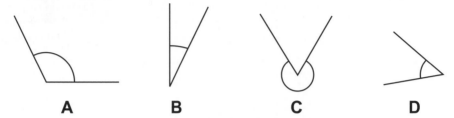

A   **B**   **C**   **D**

In the boxes, write the letter of the angle that is:

The smallest ☐   A reflex angle ☐   Obtuse ☐

___
1 mark

2) Look at the diagram. The shape starts in Position 1.
It is then rotated **90°**. It finishes in Position 2.

Position 1

Position 2

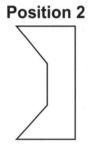

In which direction has the shape been rotated? Tick the box.

Clockwise

Anticlockwise

How many more degrees would the shape need to be rotated
(in the same direction) to bring it back to Position 1?

.......................°

___
2 marks

3) Without measuring, match up the angles with the diagrams and terms.
One has been done for you.

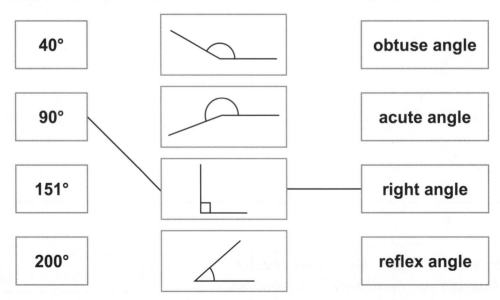

40°		obtuse angle
90°		acute angle
151°		right angle
200°		reflex angle

___
2 marks

Angles

4) Measure the two **obtuse** angles inside this shape accurately.

   Use a protractor.

   Write the angles in the right places inside the shape.

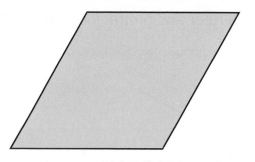

_____
1 mark

5) Measure **all** three angles inside this shape accurately.

   Use a protractor.

   Write the angles in the right places inside the shape.

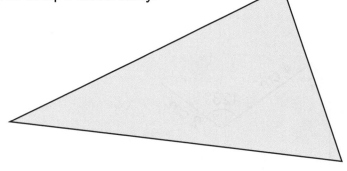

_____
2 marks

6) Draw the following angles using a ruler and a protractor.

A freshly sharpened pencil will make your diagrams much more accurate.

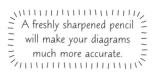 **105°**

 **68°**

 **270°**

_____
3 marks

Section 1 — Geometry

8

Angles

7) Use a ruler and protractor to accurately draw the diagrams in the space below.

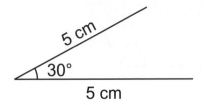

2 marks

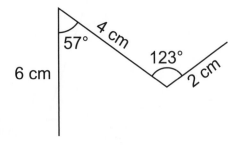

3 marks

8) Janika has described her favourite shape below.

> **It has only two right angles.**
>
> **It has one reflex angle.**
>
> **It has no obtuse angles.**

Circle the shape below that could be Janika's favourite shape.

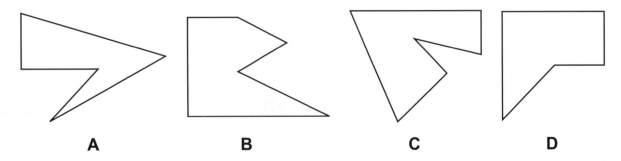

A	B	C	D

1 mark

A Trimeasuretops can handle any kind of angle it comes across. Can you? Tick the box.

Angle Calculations

On the next few pages you'll have to find angles __without__ measuring them with a protractor.

1) Nikola wants to find the reflex angle, R, shown in the diagram.

He measures the angle shown as 75°.

Find the size of angle R. This question has been done for you.

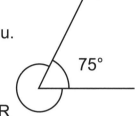

R + 75° = 360° ⟵ Angles around a point add up to 360°.

R = 360° − 75°

R = ...285........ °

R

Not drawn accurately

2) Eddie measures the angles in a triangle.

He says the angles are 60°, 70° and 80°.

Without measuring, explain why Eddie **cannot** be correct.

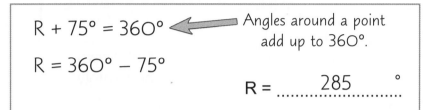

Not drawn accurately

80°

70°

60°

....

....

1 mark

3) The rectangle below has been split into two triangles.

Work out the size of angle A. Show your working in the box.

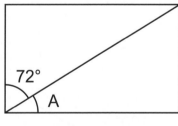

72°

A

Not drawn accurately

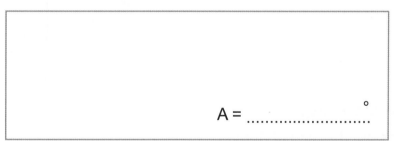

A = ... °

2 marks

4) Work out the size of angle X in this diagram.

Show your working in the box.

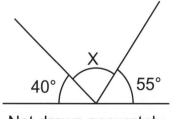

40°   X   55°

Not drawn accurately

X = ... °

2 marks

Angle Calculations

5) A right angle is split into three angles, as shown.
   Work out the size of angle C.
   Show your working in the box.

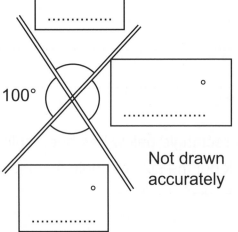

Not drawn
accurately

C = ...°

2 marks

6) The diagram shows a map of two straight roads.
   One of the angles on the diagram is shown.
   Work out the other angles.
   Write your answers in the boxes.

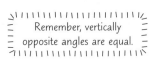

Remember, vertically
opposite angles are equal.

100°

..............°

..............°

..............°

Not drawn
accurately

2 marks

7) Look at the diagram.
   Work out the size of angle L.
   Show your working in the box.

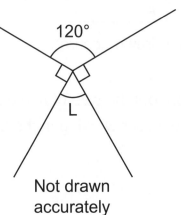

120°

L

Not drawn
accurately

L = ...°

2 marks

Angle Calculations

8) Look at the diagram.

   Are these statements true or false? Circle the answers.

   Angles A and B add up to 180°.　　　**TRUE / FALSE**

   Angles C and D add up to 180°.　　　**TRUE / FALSE**

   Angles C and E are equal.　　　　　**TRUE / FALSE**

   Angles E and F add up to 360°.　　　**TRUE / FALSE**

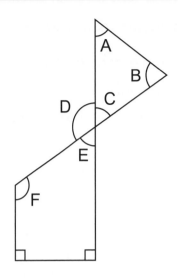

――――――
2 marks

9) Kylie has a suitcase in the shape of a **regular** polygon.

   The suitcase is standing on flat ground, as shown in the diagram.

   Work out the size of angle s. Show your working in the box.

   Not drawn accurately

   s = ... °

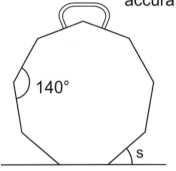

――――――
2 marks

10) The shape on the right is a parallelogram.

    A parallelogram has two pairs of equal angles.

    Work out the sizes of angle x and angle y.

    Show your working in the box.

Start by finding the angles opposite x and y.

Not drawn accurately

   x = ... °　　　　　　y = ... °

――――――
3 marks

A fully grown Trimeasuretops can find the angles
in any shape. How did you get on? Tick the box.

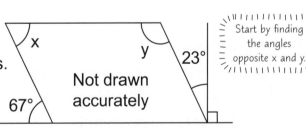

Coordinates

Coordinates are used to show a position on a grid. Give these questions on coordinates a go.

1) A triangle has vertices at (1, 2), (1, 4) and (5, 3).

   Use this information to draw this triangle on the grid below.

   The first vertex has been marked for you.

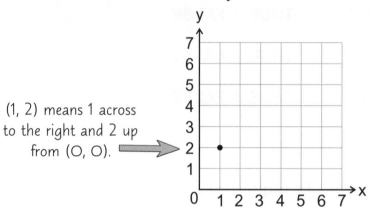

(1, 2) means 1 across to the right and 2 up from (O, O).

   What type of triangle is this? Circle your answer.

   scalene   **isosceles**   **equilateral**

   _____
   2 marks

2) Points A, B and C are three vertices of a square.

   Give the coordinates of the fourth vertex of the square.

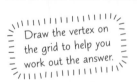

Draw the vertex on the grid to help you work out the answer.

   Coordinates: (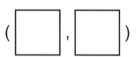 ,)

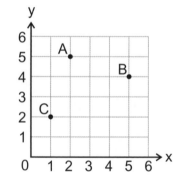

   _____
   1 mark

3) Robbie is going camping.

   The grid on the right shows a map of the area around the campsite.

   Robbie's tent is at position **B3**, and there is a large tree at position **G8**.

   Complete the sentence below:

   To get to the tree from his tent, Robbie

   needs to go .... **squares east**

   and .... **squares north.**

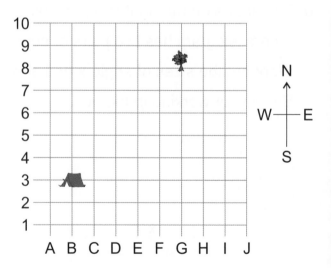

   There is a pond 3 squares east and 1 square south of the tent.

   Mark a cross on the grid to show where the pond is.

   _____
   2 marks

Coordinates

4) Look at the grid on the right.

Write down the letters that are at each of these coordinates:

(2, 1):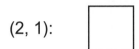

(−4, 5):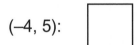

(−5, −3):

(2, −2):

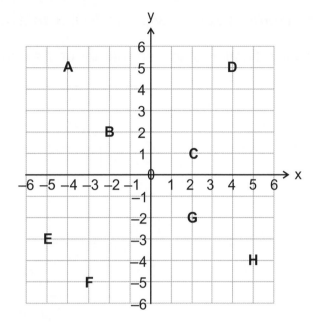

2 marks

5) In the diagram below, trapezium **B** is an identical copy of trapezium **A**.

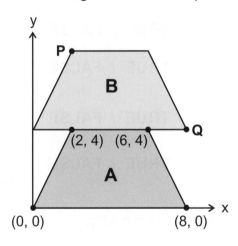

What are the coordinates of points **P** and **Q**?

Coordinates of **P**: (☐ , ☐)

Coordinates of **Q**: (☐ , ☐)

2 marks

6) This shape is symmetrical about the dotted line.

What are the coordinates of points **A**, **B** and **C**?

Coordinates of **A**: (☐ , ☐)

Coordinates of **B**: (☐ , ☐)

Coordinates of **C**: (☐ , ☐)

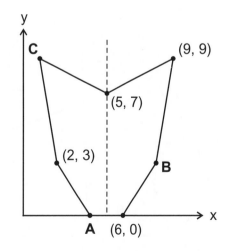

2 marks

A Trimeasuretops can find its way home from any coordinates. How did you find these questions?

Symmetry

A line of symmetry splits a shape in half, with a mirror image on either side of it.

1) Draw a reflection of this shape about the mirror line. Use a ruler.

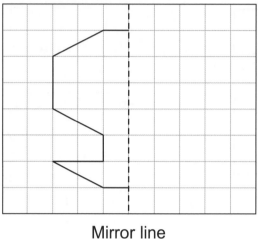

Mirror line

1 mark

2) Are these statements true or false? Circle the answers.

A regular hexagon has 6 lines of symmetry. **TRUE / FALSE**

A rhombus has no lines of symmetry. **TRUE / FALSE**

An irregular octagon has more lines
of symmetry than a regular octagon. **TRUE / FALSE**

All triangles have 3 lines of symmetry. **TRUE / FALSE**

2 marks

3) Draw lines to match these shapes with their number of lines of symmetry.
One has been done for you.

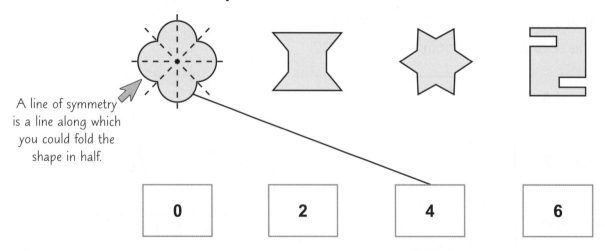

A line of symmetry
is a line along which
you could fold the
shape in half.

2 marks

*A fully grown Trimeasuretops has three beautiful
symmetrical horns. Do you like symmetry? Tick the box.*

Translation and Reflection

Translation and reflection describe the movements of shapes on a grid. Try these questions.

1) Four students have tried to reflect shape A in the dotted line.
   Which reflection was done correctly? Circle your answer.

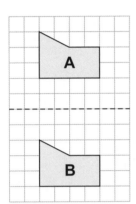 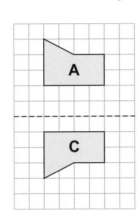 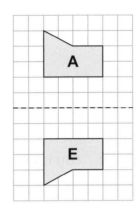

_____
1 mark

2) Two identical shapes have been drawn on this grid.

   Shape A is translated to the same position as Shape B.

   Describe this translation.

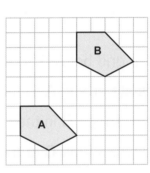

☐ squares [   ] and ☐ squares [   ]

_____
1 mark

3) Below is a shape on a coordinate grid.
   Reflect the shape in the y-axis.

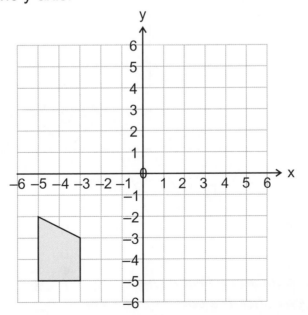

> Reflect each vertex separately and then join them up to make the reflected shape.

_____
1 mark

Section 1 — Geometry

Translation and Reflection

4) Shape **1** is reflected in the mirror line shown.

Draw the new position of Shape **1**, and label it **2**.

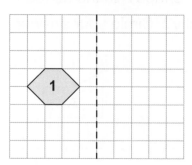

1 mark

Priya says, "You can translate Shape **1** to the same position as Shape **2**."

How would you translate Shape **1** to the position of Shape **2**?

....

1 mark

5) On the grid below:

Translate shape **A** to the **right 8** squares and **up 3** squares. Label this shape **D**.

Reflect shape **B** in the mirror line. Label this shape **E**.

Translate shape **C** to the **left 7** squares and **up 11** squares. Label this shape **F**.

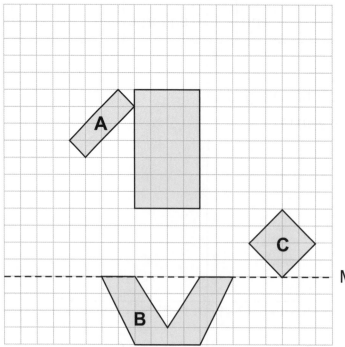

Mirror line

3 marks

A Trimeasuretops can translate and reflect a shape until it's just right. Can you? Tick the box.

Units

Have a go at these questions to practise switching between different units.

1) Draw a line to match each object to the best estimate of its length.

An ant	100 m
	2 m
The UK	30 cm
	5 mm
A person's finger	8 cm
A football pitch	950 km

2 marks

2) Bridget has taken some measurements in **centimetres**.
Write the measurements in **metres** in the boxes. One has been done for you.

300 cm = [3] m ← There are 100 cm in 1 metre, so do 300 ÷ 100.

2000 cm = [ ] m

12 500 cm = [ ] m

60 cm = [ ] m

1 cm = [ ] m

72.5 cm = [ ] m

2 marks

3) Here are some measurements. Circle the best estimate for each one.

The length of a bus	12 mm	12 cm	12 m	12 km

The capacity of a bathtub	2 ml	200 ml	2 l	200 l

The mass of a teaspoon	0.025 kg	2.5 kg	25 kg	250 kg

2 marks

Units

4) Juno has a bottle of water. She takes the following measurements:

> Height of bottle: **35 cm**
>
> Capacity: **2.1 litres**
>
> Mass (full of water): **2300 g**

What is the capacity of the bottle in **millilitres**?

.... *ml*

How tall is the bottle in **millimetres**?

.... *mm*

What is the mass of the bottle in **kilograms**
when it is full of water?

.... *kg*

_____
3 marks

5) Yusef is training for a long-distance run.
Each day, he runs **7000 m**.
How far will he have run in total after **four days**? Give your answer in km.

.... *km*

After how many days will he have run a total of **42 km**?

.... *days*

_____
2 marks

6) Bertie rides his bike to school.
Bertie's bike weighs 20 000 g. How many **kilograms** is this? Tick the box.

2 kg ☐　　　**20 kg** ☐　　　**200 kg** ☐　　　**2000 kg** ☐

Bertie lives **3 kilometres** away from his school.
How many **centimetres** is this? Tick the box.

3000 cm ☐　　**30 000 cm** ☐　　**300 000 cm** ☐　　**3 000 000 cm** ☐

_____
2 marks

Units

7) Carter is baking a cake. He has bought **1 kg** of flour and **500 g** of butter.

He uses **three quarters** of the flour.

Always pay attention to the units you need to give your answer in.

How much flour has he used? Give your answer in **grams**.

.... *g*

He uses **half** of the butter.

How much butter has he used? Give your answer in **kilograms**.

.... *kg*   _____
2 marks

8) Noor cuts a **15 cm** piece of string in **half**.

How long is each piece? Give your answer in **millimetres**.

.... *mm*   _____
1 mark

9) Mr Edward's class are building dinosaurs out of modelling clay.

He has **2.4 kg** of clay. He divides it equally between **six** groups.

How many **grams** of clay does each group get?

.... *g*   _____
1 mark

10) Vera has made **3.3 litres** of smoothie.

She drinks **six** cups of the smoothie. Each cup contains **250 ml** of smoothie.

How much smoothie is left? Give your answer in **litres**.

Show your working in the box.

.... *litres*   _____
2 marks

Section 2 — Measurement

Units

11) Here are some measurements in **metric** units.

Circle the **imperial** measurement that is the closest **estimate** for the measurement.

| 10 metres | **3 feet** | **30 feet** | **300 feet** | **3000 feet** |

| 5 litres | **0.1 pints** | **1 pint** | **10 pints** | **100 pints** |

| 300 grams | **0.012 ounces** | **0.12 ounces** | **1.2 ounces** | **12 ounces** |

| 0.8 kilometres | **0.5 miles** | **5 miles** | **50 miles** | **500 miles** |

| 50 kilograms | **1 pound** | **10 pounds** | **100 pounds** | **1000 pounds** |

| 100 centimetres | **4 inches** | **40 inches** | **400 inches** | **4000 inches** |

3 marks

12) Kamran is following a recipe. The recipe asks for **3 tablespoons** of ketchup.

Use the conversion 1 tablespoon ≈ 15 ml to work out
how many millilitres of ketchup he should use.

.... *ml*

1 mark

13) 1 foot is approximately the same as 30 centimetres.

Suzie is **5 feet** tall. Approximately how tall is she in **cm**?

.... *cm*

Her pet dog Rufus is **1.5 feet** tall. Approximately how tall is this in **cm**?

.... *cm*

2 marks

Units

14) The graph below can be used to convert between litres and gallons.

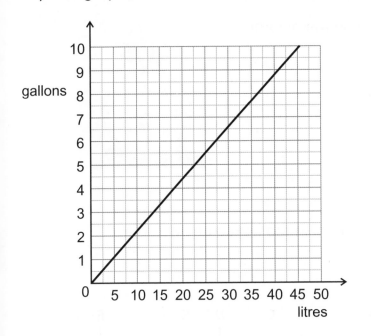

Fill in the missing numbers in the boxes:

45 litres ≈ ☐ gallons

☐ litres ≈ 4.5 gallons

27.5 litres ≈ ☐ gallons

_____
2 marks

Gary has **6** containers of fuel. Each one holds **5 litres**.

Approximately how many **gallons** of fuel does he have altogether?

.... *gallons*

_____
1 mark

15) There are 16 ounces in 1 pound. 1 kilogram is approximately 2 pounds.

A box weighs **80 ounces**. Work out roughly how many **kilograms** it weighs.

Show your working in the box.

> Convert 80 ounces into pounds first.

.... *kg*

_____
2 marks

A Trimeasuretops weighs roughly the same as 100 humans! Have you approximately mastered this topic?

Section 2 — Measurement

Reading Scales

You need to be happy reading scales that measure length, mass and volume — give it a go here.

1) Jodie is weighing out some flour, as shown in the diagram.

How much flour is on the scales?

Give your answer to the **nearest 100 grams**.

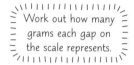 Work out how many grams each gap on the scale represents.

.... *g*

_____
1 mark

2) Write the letter that matches each measurement in the boxes below.

The diagram is not drawn to scale.

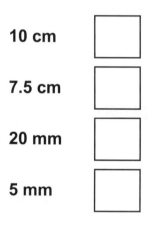

10 cm ☐

7.5 cm ☐

20 mm ☐

5 mm ☐

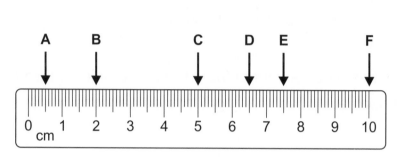

_____
2 marks

3) Dr Farlow is measuring three liquids, **A**, **B** and **C**.

She pours each one into a test tube.

The tubes are marked with volume measurements in **millilitres**.

Fill in the boxes to show how many millilitres of each liquid there are.

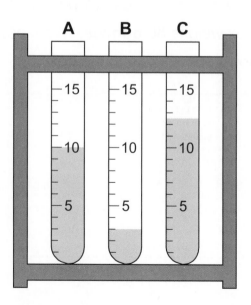

A: ☐ *ml*

B: ☐ *ml*

C: ☐ *ml*

_____
2 marks

Reading Scales

4) Amirah weighs **seven** identical pieces of fruit together.

The reading is shown on the right.

How much does **each** piece of fruit weigh?

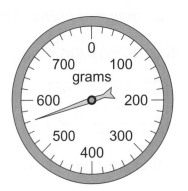

.... *g*

5) An ancient treasure has been stolen. The four suspects are shown below.

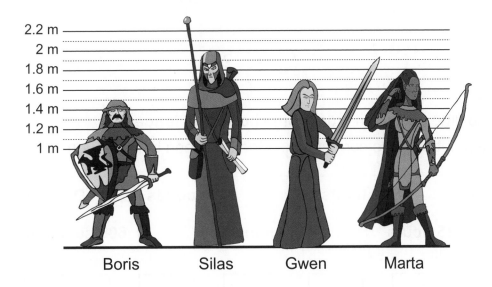

The evidence shows that the thief is **1.7 m** tall.

Who stole the ancient treasure? Circle your answer.

Boris	Silas	Gwen	Marta

A witness says: "The thief had help from someone. I couldn't see their faces, but I did see that the **difference** in their heights was **0.2 m**."

Who helped the thief to steal the treasure? Circle your answer.

Boris	Silas	Gwen	Marta

2 marks

A Trimeasuretops is never far away from some kind of measuring scale. How are your measuring skills?

Section 2 — Measurement

Time

Time can be shown in different ways. Try these questions to make sure you know them all.

1) What time does this digital display show? Write your answer in words.

`09:30` ....
1 mark

Draw this time on the clock face below.

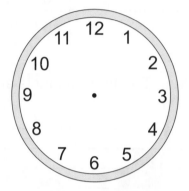

Remember that the position of the hour hand depends on the minutes as well as the hour.

1 mark

2) Put these time periods in order from **shortest** to **longest**.

Write each letter in the correct box. One has been done for you.

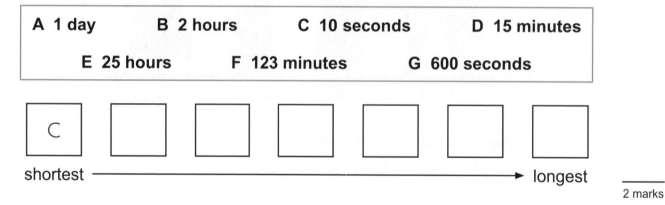

A 1 day	**B 2 hours**	**C 10 seconds**	**D 15 minutes**
E 25 hours	**F 123 minutes**	**G 600 seconds**	

C						

shortest ⟶ longest
2 marks

3) Annie went out for the day. The clock on the right shows the time when she got back in the **evening**.

Write this time as a 24-hour digital time.

`   :   `

Annie left at **7:00** in the **morning**. How long was she out for? Fill in the boxes.

[   ] hours and [   ] minutes
2 marks

Time

4) Caterina wants to travel from Appley Bridge to Daisy Hill.
   Part of the train timetable is shown below.

Appley Bridge	12.04	13.06	13.31
Daisy Hill	12.33	13.35	14.00

How long does the train take to go from Appley Bridge to Daisy Hill?

.... *minutes*

A later train departs Appley Bridge at **quarter past three** in the afternoon.
What time does it arrive at Daisy Hill? Give your answer in words.

....

2 marks

5) London is **4 hours ahead** of New York.
   Draw lines between the times in London and the matching times in New York.
   All the times are given in **12-hour** format. One has been done for you.

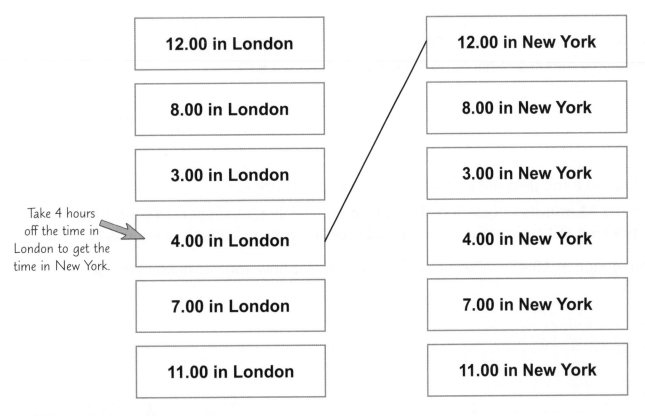

Take 4 hours off the time in London to get the time in New York.

12.00 in London	12.00 in New York
8.00 in London	8.00 in New York
3.00 in London	3.00 in New York
4.00 in London	4.00 in New York
7.00 in London	7.00 in New York
11.00 in London	11.00 in New York

2 marks

Time

6) Barney and Jo both started their homework at **6.30 pm**.

Barney finished at **8.23 pm**. Jo took **half an hour longer** than Barney.

How long did they each take to finish the homework? Fill in the boxes.

Barney: [ ] hour(s), [ ] minutes

Jo: [ ] hour(s), [ ] minutes

2 marks

7) Rocco wants to book an appointment at the dentist.

The dentist's appointment slots are shown below.

Time	8.30 - 9.15	9.15 - 10.00	10.00 - 10.45	10.45 - 11.30	11.30 - 12.15
Booked?	Available	Available	Booked	Booked	Available

Rocco needs to leave the dentist **by 11.00**.

What is the latest available appointment he can book? Circle your answer.

| 8.30 - 9.15 | 9.15 - 10.00 | 10.00 - 10.45 | 10.45 - 11.30 | 11.30 - 12.15 |

Rocco arrives for his appointment **7 minutes** after the starting time.

How many minutes of his appointment does he have left?

.... *minutes*

2 marks

8) Polina did three different kinds of exercise one afternoon.

She did **33 minutes** of cycling, **22 minutes** of weights training and **18 minutes** of aerobics. She also took a **5 minute** break between each type of exercise.

She started at **16:47**. What time did she finish? Show your working in the box.

Think carefully about the number of breaks Polina took.

.... : ....

2 marks

Section 2 — Measurement   © *CGP — not to be photocopied*

Time

9) Tony is planning to bake a cake. He wants to make it as quickly as possible.

There are three types of cake that he could make. The time needed for **preparation**, **baking** and **decorating** each cake is shown in the table below.

Cake	Preparation Time	Baking Time	Decorating Time
Cherry Pie	1 hour 45 mins	25 mins	30 mins
Swiss Roll	1 hour 10 mins	40 mins	40 mins
Apple Cake	35 mins	1 hour 15 mins	35 mins

Which cake takes the **least** amount of time to make? Circle your answer.

Cherry Pie	**Swiss Roll**	**Apple Cake**

Use the box below for your working out.

2 marks

Ruby offers to help Tony make the **Swiss Roll**.

With her help, the **preparation** and **decorating** times are reduced by **half**.

How many **minutes** does the Swiss Roll take to make with Ruby's help?

Show your working in the box.

.... *minutes*

2 marks

Trimeasuretops have been around since the dawn of time, so they're experts at time questions. Are you?

Section 2 — Measurement

Money

Have a go at the questions on this page to see how well you can deal with money.

1) Change these amounts into pounds and pence. One has been done for you.

512p = £ 5.12

512 ÷ 100

125p = £ .

350p = £ .

1233p = £ .

1051p = £ .

2002p = £ .

2 marks

2) Chidi has a **£5** note. He uses it to pay for a book that costs **£3.25**.
How much change will Chidi get?

£ ....

Chidi also has a lot of £1 coins.
He wants to buy **eight** pens. Each pen costs **£1.50**.
How many £1 coins will he need to pay for these pens?

....

2 marks

3) Ship-Shape Sailing offers cruises around a lake.
The ticket prices are shown on the right.

Jon wants to buy 1 adult and 1 child ticket.
How much will this cost?

Cruise Tickets
Child: £6.50
Adult: £12.30
Family: £35 (2 adults + 3 children)

£ ....

1 mark

How much is saved by buying a family ticket
compared with buying 2 adult and 3 child tickets?
Show your working in the box.

£ ....

2 marks

Perimeter and Area

Find out how well you can calculate the perimeters and areas of shapes with these questions.

1) Work out the perimeter of this triangle.

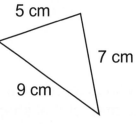

5 cm

7 cm

9 cm

.... *cm*

Not drawn to scale

_____
1 mark

2) A square has sides of length 5 cm.
   What is the **area** of the square?

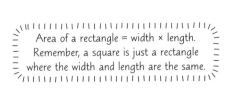

Area of a rectangle = width × length.
Remember, a square is just a rectangle
where the width and length are the same.

.... *cm²*

_____
1 mark

3) Use your ruler to measure the perimeter of this shape.
   Give your answer to the nearest whole centimetre.

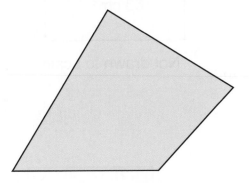

.... *cm*

_____
1 mark

4) The shape on the right is a **regular pentagon**.
   What is its perimeter? Show your working in the box.

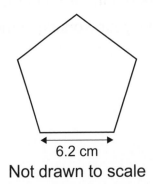

6.2 cm

Not drawn to scale

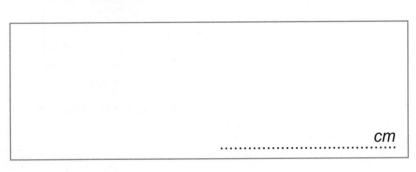

.... *cm*

_____
2 marks

© CGP — not to be photocopied

Section 2 — Measurement

Perimeter and Area

5) Simeon has drawn five different shapes on the square grid shown on the right.

Not actual size

1 cm

Draw lines to match the letter of each shape to the area of that shape.

A	B	C	D	E

4 cm²	5 cm²	6 cm²	7 cm²	8 cm²

2 marks

6) A rectangle has a height of **7 cm** and an area of **63 cm²**.

Work out the **perimeter** of the rectangle.

Show your working in the box.

Start by using the area and height to work out the missing side lengths.

.... *cm*

Area = 63 cm²

7 cm

Not drawn to scale

2 marks

7) This shaded shape has been made by cutting a square out of a rectangle.

Work out the **area** of the shaded shape.

Show your working in the box.

11 cm

3 cm

8 cm

Not drawn to scale

.... *cm²*

2 marks

Perimeter and Area

8) Here is a rectangle. Use a ruler to accurately measure the rectangle's length and width.

Fill in the boxes with these measurements.

Work out the perimeter and area of the rectangle.

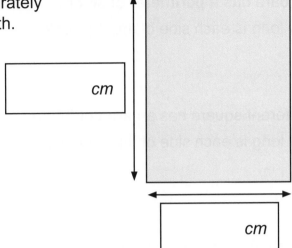

Perimeter: .... cm   Area: .... cm²

3 marks

9) The diagram below shows the plan of a playground.
Each square on the grid is **1 m** wide.

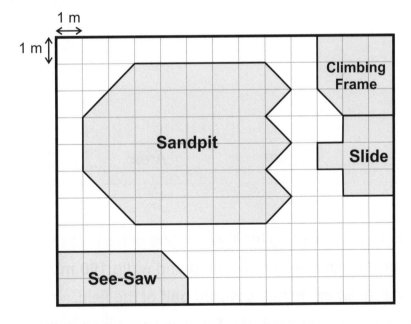

What is the total area covered by the climbing frame, slide and see-saw?

.... m²

What is the area of the sandpit?

.... m²

2 marks

Perimeter and Area

10) A square has a **perimeter** of **36 cm**.

How long is each side of this square?

.... cm

A different square has an **area** of **36 cm²**.
How long is each side of this square?

.... cm

11) A 'T' shape is made by joining two rectangles together.

Work out the **perimeter** and **area** of this shape.

Use the box below for your working out.

You'll need to work out
the missing side lengths.

11 cm

4 cm | 3 cm   3 cm

Not drawn
to scale

12 cm

Perimeter: .... cm   Area: .... cm²

12) Henry is a farmer. He is spreading fertiliser on one of his fields.

The field is a rectangle with a length of **200 m** and width **100 m**.

He runs out of fertiliser when he has covered **half** of the field.

What area of the field is left uncovered? Show your working in the box.

.... m²

Perimeter and Area

13) Find the area of this triangle.

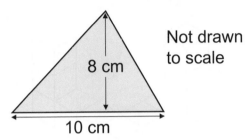

Not drawn to scale

.... cm²

1 mark

14) Francine wants to work out the area of this parallelogram.

She works out the area as **30 cm²**.

Explain why Francine's answer is **wrong** and write the correct area in the box.

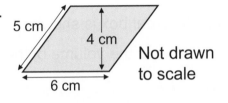

Not drawn to scale

....

....

....

Correct Area:

.... cm²

2 marks

15) Ms Chan's classroom is in the shape of a parallelogram.

She marks off part of the room to be the 'reading corner', and the rest of the room is the 'learning zone'.

What is the area of the learning zone? Show your working in the box.

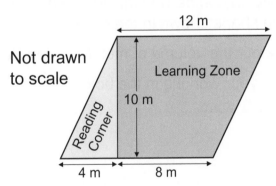

Not drawn to scale

.... m²

2 marks

For a Trimeasuretops, perimeter is an area of expertise. How did you find this topic? Tick the box.

© CGP — not to be photocopied

Section 2 — Measurement

Volume

Volume is just the amount of space a shape takes up. Have a go at these questions on it.

1) Diya has built the shape shown out of **1 cm³** cubes.

   What is the volume of the shape?

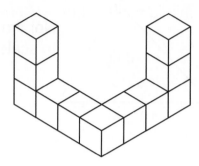

   .... *cm³*

2) A cereal box is shown in the diagram on the right.

   What is the volume of the box?

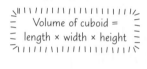

Volume of cuboid =
length × width × height

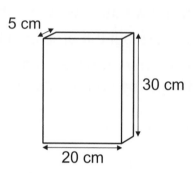

5 cm

30 cm

20 cm

Not drawn to scale

   .... *cm³*

3) A building company wants to make a metal beam
   in the shape shown in the diagram.

   Work out the volume of metal needed to make this beam.

   Show your working in the box.

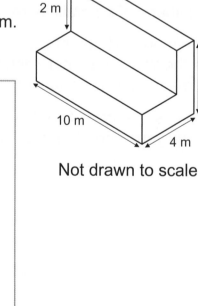

1 m

2 m

3 m

10 m

4 m

Not drawn to scale

   .... *m³*

*A Trimeasuretops can quickly work through large
volumes of these questions. Can you? Tick the box.*

Tables, Charts and Graphs

Tables, charts and graphs are all ways of recording and displaying data. Try out these questions.

1) Cynthia is a vet. One day, she counts the different pets that are brought in.
   She shows this information on a bar chart.

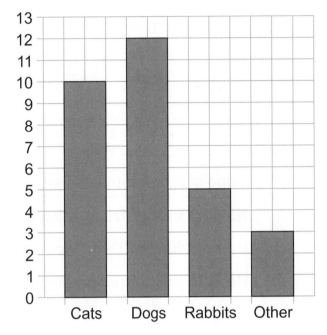

What was the most common pet brought in?
Circle your answer.

Cats   **Dogs**   **Rabbits**   **Other**

How many rabbits were brought in?

.... *rabbits*

How many **more** cats were brought in than 'Other' pets?

.... _____
                            3 marks

2) Maki runs a bakery. At lunch time, she records
   how many pieces of cake she has left.

   She fills out the first three rows
   of the pictogram on the right.

Maki has 10 pieces of coffee cake left.
Complete the pictogram.

Pieces of cake

 = 3 pieces of cake

How many pieces of cake are left in total?

                                      pieces _____
....   2 marks

Section 3 — Statistics

Tables, Charts and Graphs

3) Pablo has made a CD with his band, and is selling them at his school.

The number of CDs he sells each week is shown on the line graph.

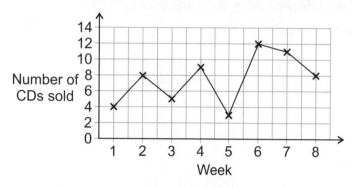

How many CDs did Pablo sell in total in the first **three** weeks?

.... CDs

1 mark

Which one of the statements below is **true**? Tick the box.

He sold more CDs in week 4 than he did in week 7. ☐

He sold fewer CDs in week 3 than he did in week 5. ☐

He sold the same number of CDs in week 2 and week 8. ☐

1 mark

4) Nate counted the number of cars of different colours that drove past his house.

He filled out this tally chart with the results.

Complete Nate's table.

Colour	Tally	Frequency
Black	ЖⅠ	6
Blue	/ⅠⅠ)	
Red	ЖⅠ ⅠⅠⅠⅠ	
Silver	ЖⅠ ⅠⅠ	
Other	ⅠⅠ)ⅠⅠ	

1 mark

Use the data to complete the bar graph. One bar has been drawn for you.

The frequency of 'Black' is 6, so find this number on the vertical axis.

Then draw a bar to the correct height.

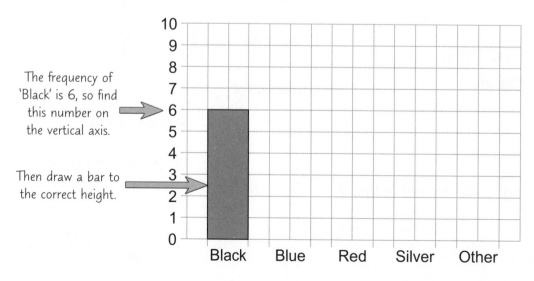

2 marks

© *CGP — not to be photocopied*

Tables, Charts and Graphs

5) The graph below shows the height of a bird above the ground after it takes off.

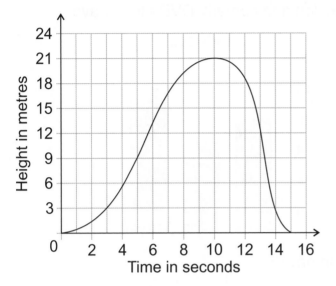

How high was the bird after **5** seconds?

.... *metres*

How long was the bird off the ground for?

.... *seconds*

What was the greatest height above the ground that the bird reached?

.... *metres*

<hr>
3 marks

6) A restaurant did a special menu for Valentine's Day.

The chef recorded the number of each dish they sold, and put the data in a table and a pictogram.

Complete both the table and the pictogram.

Dish	Number sold
Romantic Roast Beef	3
Lasagne of Love	4
Heart-Shaped Hamburgers	....
Passionate Pizza	....
Sweetheart Spaghetti	5

Romantic Roast Beef ♡ ♡

Lasagne of Love

Heart-Shaped Hamburgers ♡ ♡ ♡ ♡

Passionate Pizza ♡ ♡ ♡

Sweetheart Spaghetti

Number of dishes sold

♡ = 2 Dishes

Which dish was the most popular?

....

<hr>
3 marks

Tables, Charts and Graphs

7) Emma and Sean are comparing what films they have on DVD.

The bar charts show how many drama, action and comedy DVDs they have.

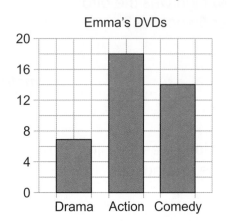

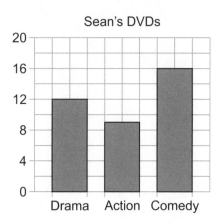

How many action DVDs does each person have?

Emma .... *DVDs*   Sean .... *DVDs*

Who has more comedy DVDs? Circle your answer.

Emma   Sean   They have the same number

2 marks

8) A group of **36** people were asked what their favourite kind of drink was.

The results are shown in the table.

Drink	Smoothie	Coffee	Tea	Juice	Milkshake
Frequency	9	6	12	5	4

Complete the pie chart below to show this information.
One sector has been drawn for you.

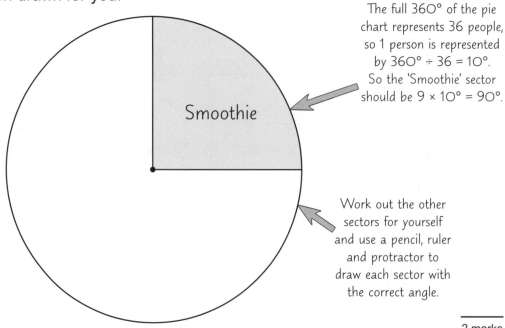

The full 360° of the pie chart represents 36 people, so 1 person is represented by 360° ÷ 36 = 10°. So the 'Smoothie' sector should be 9 × 10° = 90°.

Work out the other sectors for yourself and use a pencil, ruler and protractor to draw each sector with the correct angle.

2 marks

Tables, Charts and Graphs

9) Meena loves cats. Each day, she writes down the number of cats she sees.

The results for one week are given in the table.

Draw a line graph on the grid to show Meena's results.

You'll have to draw your own set of axes.

Day	Number of cats
Mon	3
Tue	10
Wed	5
Thu	0
Fri	2
Sat	6
Sun	5

2 marks

10) Maggie wrote down what the weather was like on **24** days.

The pie chart shows the results.

Draw lines to match the type of weather to the correct **fraction** of the total.

One has been done for you.

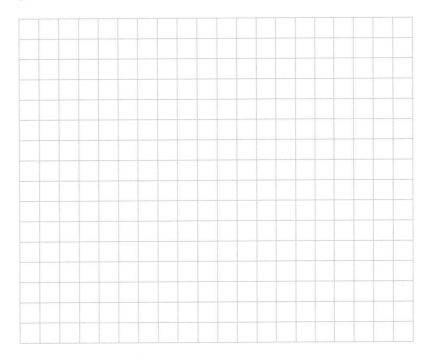

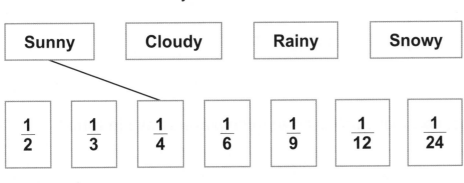

| Sunny | Cloudy | Rainy | Snowy |

$\frac{1}{2}$ $\frac{1}{3}$ $\frac{1}{4}$ $\frac{1}{6}$ $\frac{1}{9}$ $\frac{1}{12}$ $\frac{1}{24}$

For each type of weather, think about how many sectors of that size you would need to make a whole circle.

2 marks

Fill in the table.

Weather	Sunny	Cloudy	Rainy	Snowy
Number of Days				

2 marks

Tables, Charts and Graphs

11) Ethan, Grace and Tamati are playing a game.

They each start with 100 points, and can gain or lose points in each round.

The graph below is drawn to show how many points they have after each round.

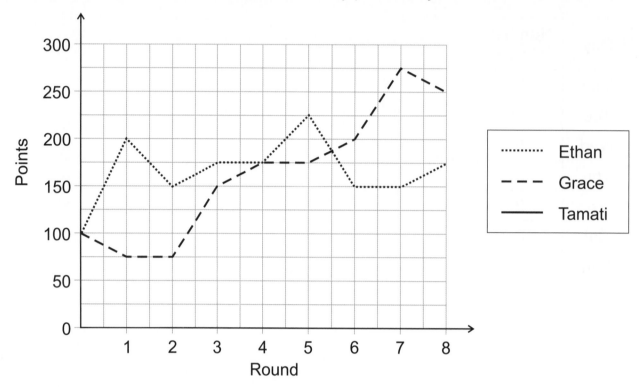

The table below shows Tamati's score at the end of each round.

Round	1	2	3	4	5	6	7	8
Score	150	200	225	125	125	175	225	200

Use this information to draw a line graph for Tamati on the diagram above.

_____
2 marks

Who had the **lowest** score at the end of round 6?

....

At the **end** of the game, how many points do all three players have **in total**?

.... *points*
_____
2 marks

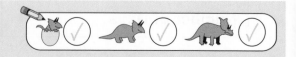

Analysing Data

Analysing data just means looking at it or doing calculations to work out what it's showing.

1) Khadija rolls a 6-sided dice **eight** times. The results are given here:

3   4   6   1   3   5   6   4

Work out the mean of the results.

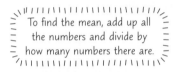
To find the mean, add up all
the numbers and divide by
how many numbers there are.

....

—————

1 mark

2) A school has four language clubs: French, German, Italian and Spanish.

The graph shows the number of people in each club.

Work out the mean of this data. Show your working in the box.

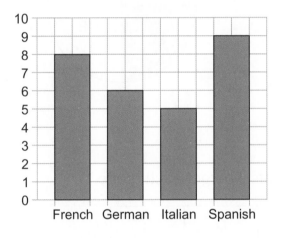

....

—————

2 marks

3) Brian wants to know the mean age of his friends.

One of his friends is 8 years old.

Four of his friends are 10 years old.

Two of his friends are 11 years old.

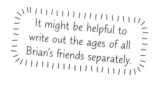
It might be helpful to
write out the ages of all
Brian's friends separately.

Work out the mean age of Brian's friends. Show your working in the box.

years old

....

—————

2 marks

© *CGP — not to be photocopied*   *Section 3 — Statistics*

Analysing Data

4) Satoru counted the number of characters in **four** different TV shows.

   He worked out that the mean number of characters was **8**.

   In **total**, how many characters were there in all four TV shows?

   .... *characters*

   The first three shows had **10** characters, **7** characters and **9** characters.

   How many characters were in the last show?

   .... *characters*
   _____
   2 marks

5) A teacher is writing reports for the students in her class.

   She has to give each student
   an effort grade of **A**, **B**, **C**, **D** or **E**.

   The pie chart shows the number
   of students that got each grade.

   6 students got an effort grade of **C**.

   How many students are there in the class in total?

   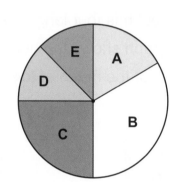

   .... *students*
   _____
   1 mark

   Complete the table showing the number of students who got each grade.

Grade	A	B	C	D	E
Number of students	4		6		

   _____
   2 marks

6) The data set below has a mean of **5**.
   Fill in the missing number in the box.

   The first step is to work out the total of all the numbers using the mean.

   7,   4,   2,   ⬚   8,   3,   7,   6

   Show your working in the box below.

   _____
   2 marks

Analysing Data

7) Draw lines to match the data set to the correct mean.
One has been done for you.

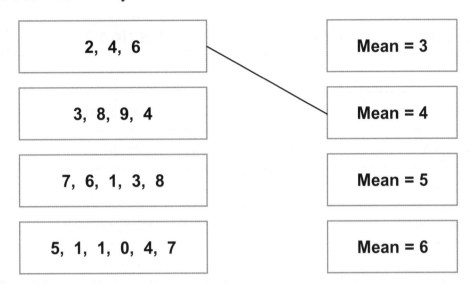

2, 4, 6		Mean = 3
3, 8, 9, 4		Mean = 4
7, 6, 1, 3, 8		Mean = 5
5, 1, 1, 0, 4, 7		Mean = 6

2 marks

8) Vicky is trying to choose between two films to watch.
She looks up some review scores for each of the two films, shown below.
The scores are all out of 5 stars.

Film A	4, 2, 3, 3, 4, 0, 4, 4
Film B	5, 4, 2, 2, 3, 4, 5, 5, 3, 4

Which film has the highest mean score? Circle: **Film A**   **Film B**

Show your working in the box below.

2 marks

A fully grown Trimeasuretops is a lean, mean, data-analysing machine. Are you? Tick the box.

Section 3 — Statistics

Scoresheet

Fill in your scores below as you work through the book.
Once you get to the end of each section, find your total marks to see how you're getting on.

Section 1	Score
2D Shapes	/ 12
Circles	/ 6
3D Shapes	/ 9
Angles	/ 17
Angle Calculations	/ 18
Coordinates	/ 11
Symmetry	/ 5
Translation and Reflection	/ 8
Total for Section 1	**/ 86**

Section 2	Score
Units	/ 30
Reading Scales	/ 8
Time	/ 20
Money	/ 7
Perimeter and Area	/ 29
Volume	/ 4
Total for Section 2	**/ 98**
Section 3	**Score**
Tables, Charts and Graphs	/ 30
Analysing Data	/ 16
Total for Section 3	**/ 46**

Total for Book	**/ 230**

Look at your total score to see how you're
doing and where you need more practice:

0 – 129 — Don't worry if you got lots wrong.
Revise the skills that you're struggling
with and then have another go.

130 – 179 — You're doing well. Take a look
back at any sections you're
struggling with and have another
go to make sure you're happy.

180 – 230 — You're doing really well.
Give yourself a pat on the back.